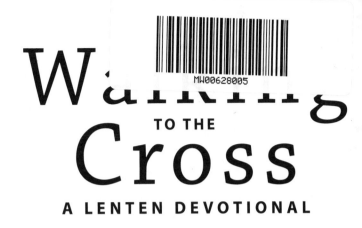

Walking
TO THE
Cross
A LENTEN DEVOTIONAL

Butch Odom

Church Health | Memphis, TN

About Church Health

Church Health seeks to reclaim the church's biblical commitment to care for our bodies and our spirits. Long recognized as a national model for serving the uninsured, Church Health has spent years connecting people of faith and their congregations with quality health resources and educational experiences. To learn more about the organization, visit ChurchHealth.org. To learn more about our magazine on health ministry, *Church Health Reader*, visit CHReader.org.

About the Author

William L. "Butch" Odom, Jr. has served in a variety of roles in his more than 20 years of service at Church Health. He is the author of *Walking to the Manger: An Advent Devotional*, *Have a Blessed Day: A Year of Daily Devotions from the Church Health Center* and several pieces for *Church Health Reader*, including the award-winning reflection, "Setting a New Table." Butch and his wife, Debbie, live in Memphis where they are members of First Congregational Church.

Walking to the Cross: A Lenten Devotional

© 2012 Church Health Center, Inc. Memphis, TN
Third Printing, 2016

ISBN: 978-0-615-59883-3

Printed in the United States of America.

Church Health is proud to publish this resource using recycled materials.

Cover and design by Lizy Heard.

The primary objective of *Walking to the Cross* is to help your community incorporate healthy habits into their lives during the season of Lent. *Walking to the Cross* was first published in *Church Health Reader* in 2010. For more resources for you and your church, visit *Church Health Reader* at CHReader.org.

To my wife Debbie
who walks with me each step of the way

Introduction

About *Walking to the Cross*

Walking to the Cross is a 40-day devotional designed for the Christian season of Lent. It invites you to make walking, reflecting and prayer a part of your daily Lenten practice. Just as Jesus traveled the long journey to the cross, we believe that walking is an act of spiritual and physical devotion.

How to Use *Walking to the Cross*

Every week begins with a psalm and the opportunity to set a "movement goal," or a reasonable physical challenge for yourself. Your movement goal may be taking more steps each day, going for a daily walk, wearing a pedometer to count the distance you walk each day, or any other challenge you wish to set for yourself.

Each day in Lent also offers a passage of Scripture along with a thought and a prayer. You may read any time during the day, or you may reflect on them while engaged in your chosen physical activity. Each page includes journal space for you to track the progress toward your goals and note any personal challenges or successes.

As you walk with Christ through the season of Lent, we pray that you may become healthier in body and spirit with each step you take toward the cross.

Week 1

The Fast I Choose

You desire truth in the inward being; therefore teach me wisdom in my secret heart.

—Psalm 51:6

Movement Goal

....

....

....

....

Ash Wednesday

*Yet even now, says the L*ORD*, return to me with all your heart, with fasting, with weeping, and with mourning; rend your hearts and not your clothing. Return to the L*ORD*, your God, for he is gracious and merciful, slow to anger, and abounding in steadfast love, and relents from punishing.* — Joel 2:12–13

Reflection

As a common part of our life journey, each of us has strayed from God. Lent provides us with an opportunity to embark on a new journey toward God all over again. In keeping with this idea of journeying, I hope you will consider physically and metaphorically walking toward the cross.

Prayer

Gracious and merciful God, join me as I embark on this journey and create in me a new heart. AMEN.

Personal Reflection

Thursday

Is this not the fast I choose: to loose the bonds of injustice, to undo the thongs of the yoke, to let the oppressed go free, and to break every yoke? Is it not to share your bread with the hungry, and bring the homeless poor into your house; when you see the naked, to cover them, and not to hide yourself from your own kin? — Isaiah 58:6–7

Reflection
I think it is easy to think of Lent as an ongoing, private conversation between you and God. But, this passage reminds us of the communal nature of our faith—how our faithful walk with God involves assisting our neighbors in the removal of the barriers they are facing.

Prayer
Gracious and merciful God, help my eyes see the plight of my neighbors more clearly. AMEN.

Personal Reflection

Friday

*Then you shall call, and the L*ORD *will answer; you shall cry for help, and he will say, "Here I am". If you remove the yoke from among you, the pointing of the finger, the speaking of evil, if you offer food to the hungry and satisfy the needs of the afflicted, then your light shall rise in the darkness and your gloom will be like the noonday.* — Isaiah 58:9–10

Reflection
Our lights shine as we help others' lights shine, but this passage asks that we "satisfy the needs of the afflicted." Determining the actual needs of our neighbors, however, is quite difficult. Feeding someone is easy. Feeding someone a nutritious, healthy meal requires intentionality, forethought and willingness.

Prayer
Gracious and merciful God, help me understand the true needs of my neighbors so my help may satisfy the need you see. AMEN.

Personal Reflection

....

....

....

....

Saturday

"Do not store up for yourselves treasures on earth, where moth and rust consume and where thieves break in and steal; but store up for yourselves treasures in heaven, where neither moth nor rust consumes and where thieves do not break in and steal. For where your treasure is, there your heart will be also."
— Matthew 6:19–21

Reflection
The fast we are asked to choose is one which looks deeply at the needs of our neighbors. It is a fast aimed at justice for all rather than denial of self. It is a fast that pierces the dark places of our world. It is a fast that places priorities in the right order.

Prayer
Gracious and merciful God, the fast I choose requires your lead. Take my hand. AMEN.

Personal Reflection

....

....

....

....

Week 2

My God, My Protector

*My refuge and my fortress
is God, in whom I trust.*
—Psalm 91:2b

Movement Goal

....

....

....

....

Monday

*"...The L*ORD* brought us out of Egypt with a mighty hand and an outstretched arm, with a terrifying display of power, and with signs and wonders; and he brought us into this place and gave us this land, a land flowing with milk and honey. So now I bring the first of the fruit of the ground that you, O L*ORD*, have given me."* — Deuteronomy 26:8–10a

Reflection
I remember little of the high-school French I took, but I always liked the name for potato, *pomme de terre*, apple of the earth. My relationship with potatoes has not always been a healthy, portion-controlled one, but I remain thankful for them as they are one of my favorite foods. Thank God for your favorite fruit or vegetable today.

Prayer
Creator God, thank you for providing us with an abundance of healthy and delicious food. AMEN.

Personal Reflection

....

....

....

....

Tuesday

For [the LORD] will command his angels concerning you to guard you in all your ways. On their hands they will bear you up, so that you will not dash your foot against the stone. You will tread on the lion and the adder, the young lion and the serpent you will trample under foot. — Psalm 91:11–13

Reflection
All the electrical cords, the edges of rugs and the uneven places might become trip hazards in your daily life. Sidewalks can be notoriously uneven and sometimes covered with debris. Exercise caution so that your walking and running are safe experiences for you.

Prayer
Steadfast God, thank you for your presence beside me on all of the journeys of my life. AMEN.

Personal Reflection

....

....

....

....

Wednesday

For there is no distinction between Jew and Greek; the same Lord is Lord of all and is generous to all who call on him. For, "Everyone who calls on the name of the Lord shall be saved."
— Romans 10:12–13

Reflection

"Jesus loves me this I know, for the Bible tells me so." For most, the walk toward health is filled with both success and failure. Unfortunately, the failures often create obstacles that prevent us from restarting. Love yourself as God loves you.

Prayer

Loving God, you accept me as I am. Help me better accept myself. AMEN.

Personal Reflection

....

....

....

....

Thursday

Jesus, full of the Holy Spirit, returned from the Jordan and was led by the Spirit in the wilderness, where for forty days he was tempted by the devil. He ate nothing at all during those days, and when they were over, he was famished. — Luke 4:1–2

Reflection

Except for a few times prior to special medical procedures, I have never been hungry. While I have used the word famished to describe how I feel, I have never gone to bed hungry as do so many people in our world.

Prayer

Almighty God, I enjoy an abundant life. Keep me mindful of those less fortunate than I am. AMEN.

Personal Reflection

....

....

....

....

Friday

The devil said to [Jesus], "If you are the Son of God, command this stone to become a loaf of bread." Jesus answered him, "It is written, 'One does not live by bread alone.'" — Luke 4:3–4

Reflection
Quick fixes dominate our culture. The spiritual journey requires time and patience. Pause to take in spiritual sustenance, to proclaim personal Sabbath time. Living abundantly requires regular eating from the spiritual food group, too.

Prayer
God of abundance, help me consume the spiritual nourishment you freely offer me. AMEN.

Personal Reflection

....

....

....

....

Saturday

Then the devil led [Jesus] up and showed him in an instant all the kingdoms of the world. And the devil said to him, "To you I will give their glory and all this authority; for it has been given over to me, and I give it to anyone I please. If you, then, will worship me, it will all be yours." Jesus answered him, "It is written, 'Worship the Lord your God, and serve only him.'" — Luke 4:5–8

Reflection
Temptation, whether obvious or insidious, is a challenging part of living. How one handles temptation, through strength of character and forgiveness of self, will determine in large part one's success.

Prayer
Forgiving God, help me better forgive myself, as you have already forgiven me. AMEN.

Personal Reflection

....

....

....

....

Week 3

In God I Trust

The LORD is my light and
my salvation; whom shall I fear?
—Psalm 27:1a

Movement Goal

Monday

[The Lᴏʀᴅ] brought [Abram] outside and said, "Look toward heaven and count the stars, if you are able to count them." Then he said to him, "So shall your descendants be." And [Abram] believed the Lᴏʀᴅ; and the Lᴏʀᴅ reckoned it to him as righteousness. — Genesis 15:5–6

Reflection

Children in your old age! Descendents as numerous as the stars! God makes extraordinary promises to seemingly ordinary people who share a deep, abiding faith. I pray for the faith of Abraham.

Prayer

Gracious God, thank you for the promise that you will always be with me. AMEN.

Personal Reflection

....

....

....

....

Tuesday

As the sun was going down, a deep sleep fell upon Abram, and a deep and terrifying darkness descended upon him…On that day the LORD made a covenant with Abram, saying, "To your descendents I give this land…" — Genesis 15:12, 18

Reflection
I would guess that many of us won't experience the presence of God in a dream like Abraham. But the passage does allow us to remember that all of us need deep, recuperative sleep to perform at our optimum ability. Get the rest you need so you can serve God to your best ability.

Prayer
God of day and night, may your spirit quiet my mind tonight so that I can rest in your peace. AMEN.

Personal Reflection

Wednesday

The LORD is my light and my salvation; whom shall I fear? The LORD is the stronghold of my life; of whom shall I be afraid?
— Psalm 27:1

Reflection
I sometimes feel as though my life is being filmed and my actions are being judged by all around me. This can create an unintentional timidity. Psalm 27 reminds me that God strengthens me in my daily life, and I should move boldly into the days ahead of me, serving God to the best of my ability.

Prayer
Almighty God, help me walk assured in your love and support of me. AMEN.

Personal Reflection

....

....

....

....

Thursday

But our citizenship is in heaven, and it is from there that we are expecting a Savior, the Lord Jesus Christ. He will transform the body of our humiliation that it may be conformed to the body of his glory, by the power that also enables him to make all things subject to himself. — Philippians 3:20–21

Reflection
One's self image can be a help or a hindrance in his or her journey toward healthier living. Paul admonishes us to be proud of our shared heritage as children of heaven, reminding us that we are the Body of Christ first.

Prayer
Sovereign God, help me take better care of myself, keeping me mindful that there is no shame in Christ's body. AMEN.

Personal Reflection

....

....

....

....

Friday

Just as they were leaving, Peter said to Jesus, "Master, it is good for us to be here; let us make three dwellings, one for you, one for Moses, and one for Elijah"—not knowing what he said.
— Luke 9:33

Reflection
"Can we stay a little longer?" There is comfort in what is known, so it isn't surprising that Peter would want the moment of the Transfiguration to last. But life is lived in community with others, and we must trust that God remains by our side as we walk down our own hills into the unknown that lies before us.

Prayer
Loving God, I believe. Help my unbelief. AMEN.

Personal Reflection

....

....

....

....

Saturday

Just then a man from the crowd shouted, "Teacher, I beg you to look at my son; he is my only child." While he was coming, the demon dashed [the son] to the ground in convulsions. But Jesus rebuked the unclean spirit, healed the boy, and gave him back to his father. And all were astounded at the greatness of God.
— Luke 9:38, 42–43

Reflection
From this mountaintop experience of the Transfiguration which has Peter asking to stay, I imagine Jesus saying, "We cannot stay. There is too much work to do." And what is the first thing Jesus does at the bottom of the mountain? Jesus heals a child.

Prayer
Steadfast God, guide us in our work so we might be healing presences to those around us. AMEN.

Personal Reflection

Week 4

Thirst for God

God, you are my God, I see you, my soul thirsts for you; my flesh faints for you, as in a dry and weary land where there is no water.

—Psalm 63:1

Movement Goal

....

....

....

....

Monday

Lo, everyone who thirsts, come to the waters; and you that have no money, come, buy and eat! Come buy wine and milk without money and without price. Why do you spend your money for that which is not bread, and your labor for that which does not satisfy? Listen carefully to me, and eat what is good, and delight yourselves in rich food. — Isaiah 55:1

Reflection
A wine taster, who holds the wine glass up to the light, swirls and sniffs the wine, then savors a sip. In doing this, the essence of the wine is uncovered, its complexities discovered. Likewise may we savor God's Word.

Prayer
Almighty God, help me taste your Word so that it nourishes me as you desire. AMEN.

Personal Reflection

....

....

....

....

Tuesday

Seek the LORD while he may be found, call upon him while he is near; let the wicked forsake their way, and the unrighteous their thoughts; let them return to the LORD, that he may have mercy on them, and to our God, for he will abundantly pardon.
— Isaiah 55:6–7

Reflection
Forgiveness can be difficult, and yet offering and receiving forgiveness can be an important step in one's journey toward healing. While forgiveness is hard for us, this passage assures that God not only forgives but does so abundantly.

Prayer
Steadfast God, bless my efforts to do your will. Forgive the many times I fall short. AMEN.

Personal Reflection

....

....

....

....

Wednesday

For my thoughts are not your thoughts, nor are your ways my ways, says the LORD. For as the heavens are higher than the earth, so are my ways higher than your ways and my thoughts than your thoughts. — Isaiah 55:8–9

Reflection
Try as we might, God can't be fully understood, at least in this life. We can study God's Word and listen to stirring sermons, but we also have to pay close attention to that part of God residing in us.

Prayer
Ever-present God, help attune my ear to your voice inside me. AMEN.

Personal Reflection

....

....

....

....

Thursday

I do not want you to be unaware, brothers and sisters, that our ancestors were all under the cloud, and all passed through the sea, and all were baptized into Moses in the cloud and in the sea, and all ate the same spiritual food, and all drank the same spiritual drink. For they drank from the spiritual rock that followed them, and the rock was Christ. —1 Corinthians 10:1–4

Reflection
Paul, writing to the Corinthians about the Exodus, goes on to remind them about the terrible things that befell the Israelites with whom God was not pleased. This passage is a reminder that while we might read the same verses, our interpretations and resulting actions can be vastly different. We need to be gentle with one another remembering that God's thoughts are not our thoughts (Isaiah 55:8).

Prayer
Gracious God, help me love and support my neighbor. AMEN.

Personal Reflection

Friday

[Jesus] asked them, "Do you think that because these Galileans suffered in this way they were worse sinners than all other Galileans? No, I tell you; unless you repent, you will all perish as they did." — Luke 13:2–3

Reflection

Whether intentional or unintentional, we often make value judgments on those who are different from us. These value judgments often cloud our view of those left out of the systems of support we have in areas like access to health care or housing. Yet, the Hebrew word for repent, *teshuvah*, means simply return to God—return to the God whose steadfast love includes abundant pardon.

Prayer

Steadfast God, help my journey in life always be toward you. AMEN.

Personal Reflection

....

....

....

....

Saturday

[Jesus telling the parable of the fig tree says], "So he said to the gardener, 'See here! For three years I have come looking for fruit on this fig tree, and still I find none. Cut it down! Why should it be wasting this soil?' He replied, 'Sir, let it alone for one more year, until I dig around it and put manure on it.'" — Luke 13:7–8

Reflection
Gardens left unattended produce little. In our journey toward God we are, like the gardener in the parable, fertilizing our faith. May all of our journeys produce abundant blooms and branches laden with fruit.

Prayer
Gracious, loving God, may your Spirit well up inside me as I seek a closer relationship with you. AMEN.

Personal Reflection

Week 5

Estranged No More

I said, 'I will confess my transgressions to the
LORD', and you forgave the guilt of my sin."
—Psalm 32:5b

Movement Goal

....

....

....

....

Monday

The Lord said to Joshua, "Today, I have rolled away from you the disgrace of Egypt." And so this place is called Gilgal to this day. On the day after the Passover, on that very day, they ate the produce of the land, unleavened cakes and parched grain. The manna ceased on the day they ate the produce of the land, and the Israelites no longer had manna; they ate the crops of the land of Canaan that year. — Joshua 5:9, 11–12

Reflection
A locavore is a person dedicated to eating food grown and produced locally. Food from within your region needs fewer preservatives to maintain freshness and uses less fossil fuel in delivering the product to you, making it healthier for you and the planet. Let us all eat "the produce of the land" this day.

Prayer
Bounteous God, for lush fields, succulent fruits and hearty grains, I give you thanks today. AMEN.

Personal Reflection

....

....

....

....

Tuesday

From now on, therefore, we regard no one from a human point of view; even though we once knew Christ from a human point of view, we know him no longer that way. So if anyone is in Christ, there is a new creation: everything old has passed away; see everything has become new! — 2 Corinthians 5:16–17

Reflection
It is easy to look at a person as a gender or a skin color or as a member of a certain socioeconomic class. We ascribe values and prejudices to these and other traits. As people of faith, we are called to look at people through God's lens.

Prayer
Loving God, remove the scales of prejudice and presumption from my eyes so that I might see people as you do. AMEN.

Personal Reflection

....

....

....

....

Wednesday

All this is from God, who reconciled us to himself through Christ, and has given us the ministry of reconciliation; that is, in Christ God was reconciling the world to himself, not counting their trespasses against them, and entrusting the message of reconciliation to us. — 2 Corinthians 5:18–19

Reflection
Two synonyms for reconciliation are bringing together and understanding. I see my faith journey as a ministry that seeks to unite people. During your contemplative time today, consider your own ministry of reconciliation.

Prayer
Gracious God, help me better understand your will so that I might be more help to others. AMEN.

Personal Reflection

....

....

....

....

Thursday

Now all the tax collectors and sinners were coming near to listen to him. And the Pharisees and the scribes were grumbling and saying, "This fellow welcomes sinners and eats with them."
— Luke 15:1–2

Reflection
When you begin to look at people through Jesus' eyes, radical hospitality can take place. Make a conscious effort today to put on what you think is Jesus' lens and see how your world and those in it might look different.

Prayer
Understanding God, help us see your face in others as we move toward our own reconciliation. AMEN.

Personal Reflection

....

....

....

....

Friday

But when [the younger son] came to himself he said, 'How many of my father's hired hands have bread enough and to spare, but here I am dying of hunger! I will get up and go to my father, and I will say to him, "Father, I have sinned against heaven and before you; I am no longer worthy to be called your son; treat me like one of your hired hands."' — Luke 5:17–19

Reflection
Who do you see when you look at the face staring back at you in the mirror? Not only are we asked to look at others through God's lens, but we are also asked to look at ourselves in the same way. Before we can reconcile with God, we must first reconcile with ourselves.

Prayer
Parent God, just as you call us to be gentle with one another, help me be more gentle with myself. AMEN.

Personal Reflection

Saturday

So he set off and went to his father. But while he was still far off, his father saw him and was filled with compassion; he ran and put his arms around him and kissed him. — Luke 15:20

Reflection
I am convinced God is like this father standing at the edge of the driveway earnestly awaiting the return of his estranged son. God's abundant pardon is immediately available if we are able to make those first steps back toward God.

Prayer
Steadfast God, your love for me is boundless. Help me use your love to better love others as well as myself. AMEN.

Personal Reflection

....

....

....

....

Week 6

Moving Forward

The LORD has done great things
for us, and we rejoiced.
—Psalm 126:3

Movement Goal

....

....

....

....

Monday

Thus says the L<small>ORD</small>, who makes a way in the sea, a path in the mighty waters, who brings out the chariot and horse, army and warrior; they lie down, they cannot rise, they are extinguished, quenched like a wick… — Isaiah 43:16–17

Reflection
Whether or not you are walking as a part of your Lenten discipline, you will want to consider the path down which God is directing you. God can make a way for you, but it can prove challenging to discern God's will. With your faith as your armor, enjoy the journey.

Prayer
Gracious God, help me be a better listener to your voice in my life this week. AMEN.

Personal Reflection

....

....

....

....

Tuesday

I am about to do a new thing; now it springs forth, do you not perceive it? I will make a way in the wilderness and rivers in the desert. The wild animals will honor me, the jackals and ostriches; for I give water in the wilderness, rivers in the desert, to give drink to my people... — Isaiah 43:19–20

Reflection
It is easy for us to place limits on God's power, but this passage reminds us that in God, the possibilities are limitless. Expect the unexpected. Expect the impossible, for you are walking into God's plan, not yours.

Prayer
Almighty God, help me see the path toward which you are directing me. AMEN.

Personal Reflection

....

....

....

....

Wednesday

Beloved, I do not consider that I have made it my own; but this one thing I do: forgetting what lies behind and straining forward to what lies ahead, I press on toward the goal for the prize of the heavenly call of God in Christ Jesus.
— Philippians 3:13–14

Reflection
Forget what lies behind you. What a powerfully freeing line! Live as the forgiven person you are. Live knowing that your God of endless possibilities is not limited by your past so you aren't either.

Prayer
Gracious God, I have erected barriers limiting my ability to follow your lead. Help me remove them. AMEN.

Personal Reflection

....

....

....

....

Thursday

Six days before the Passover Jesus came to Bethany, the home of Lazarus, whom he had raised from the dead. There they gave a dinner for him. Martha served, and Lazarus was one of those at the table. — John 12:1–2

Reflection
Of course Martha served. And she probably cooked the meal, too. All of us need Marthas in our lives—organized, action-oriented, problem solvers. Consider the Marthas in your life and thank God for them today.

Prayer
Loving God, bless those special people in my life who provide structure, organization and results. AMEN.

Personal Reflection

Friday

Mary took a pound of costly perfume made of pure nard, anointed Jesus' feet, and wiped them with her hair. The house was filled with the fragrance of perfume. But Judas Iscariot, one of his disciples (the one who was about to betray him), said, "Why was this perfume not sold for three hundred denarii and the money given to the poor?" — John 12:3–5

Reflection
Nard came from a plant that grew in what is now India. Its value, three hundred denarii, was equivalent to a year's wages in Jesus' time, so Mary's spontaneous act of love and adoration was an extravagance that many of us might have questioned.

Prayer
Gracious God of endless possibilities, help us follow you with the zeal of Mary. AMEN.

Personal Reflection

....

....

....

....

Saturday

Jesus said, "Leave her alone. She bought it so that she might keep it for the day of my burial. You will always have the poor with you, but you do not always have me." — John 12:7–8

Reflection
Mary's generous act now serves to foreshadow Jesus' death in just a few days. In his acknowledgement of this, Jesus claims the path that God has chosen and begins his walk into God's plan.

Prayer
Loving God, where you lead, I will follow. AMEN.

Personal Reflection

Holy Week

Clarity for the Journey

You are my God, and I will give thanks to you;
you are my God, I will extol you.

—Psalm 118:28

Movement Goal

....

....

....

....

Monday

As [Jesus] rode along, people kept spreading their cloaks on the road. As he was approaching the path down from the Mount of Olives, the whole multitude of the disciples began to praise God joyfully with a loud voice for all the deeds of power that they had seen, saying, "Blessed is the king who comes in the name of the Lord! Peace in heaven, and glory in the highest heaven!"
— Luke 19:36–38

Reflection

Unlike the people laying their coats on the road, we know that this story begins anew on Easter. It always makes me pause when I consider the fleetingness of human opinion, especially on important matters. The adoration of the crowds today will turn into disdain of the highest magnitude in just a few days.

Prayer

Steadfast God, strengthen my faith so that I might be able to withstand the pull of the crowd away from you. AMEN.

Personal Reflection

....

....

....

....

Tuesday

But I trust in you, O LORD; I say, "You are my God." My times are in your hand; deliver me from the hand of my enemies and persecutors. Let your face shine upon your servant; save me in your steadfast love. — Psalm 31:14–16

Reflection

"God is my copilot." While catchy, this is not my favorite bumper sticker. It suggests that God is assisting us on a journey we are leading, where we know the final destination. I hope your journey this Lenten season has helped you to see more clearly God's direction and destination for your life.

Prayer

Almighty God, lead where you will lead me. Help me more closely follow you. AMEN.

Personal Reflection

....

....

....

....

Wednesday

Let the same mind be in you that was in Christ Jesus, who, though he was in the form of God, did not regard equality with God as something to be exploited, but emptied himself, taking the form of a slave, being born in human likeness. And being found in human form, he humbled himself and became obedient to the point of death, even death on a cross. — Philippians 2:5–8

Reflection

"Become as Christ!" A tall order for all of us. Yet, I hope your Lenten journey has led you to a new understanding of God's will for your life. May you recognize God's calling in your life, and like Christ, may you walk boldly into that vision.

Prayer

Loving God, may the teachings and actions of Christ Jesus more deeply inform and direct my life. AMEN.

Personal Reflection

Maundy Thursday

Jesus, knowing that the Father had given all things into his hands, and that he had come from God and was going to God, got up from the table, took off his outer robe, and tied a towel around himself. Then he poured water into a basin and began to wash the disciples' feet and to wipe them with the towel that was tied around him. — John 13:3–5

Reflection
To wash someone's feet, both parties have to become vulnerable to one another. A servant to the end, Christ poured out his love for us. May we be willing to risk allowing his intimate touch in our lives.

Prayer
Understanding God, help me be more vulnerable to your presence in my life so that I might walk closer to you. AMEN.

Personal Reflection

....

....

....

....

Good Friday

When they came to the place that is called The Skull, they crucified Jesus there with the criminals, one on his right and one on his left. Then Jesus said, "Father, forgive them; for they do not know what they are doing." And they cast lots to divide his clothing. — Luke 23:33–34

Reflection
Our Lenten journey ends at the foot of the cross with Christ's words of piercing clarity. To those who whipped him and nailed him to the cross, to the multitudes who laid their coats down on Sunday just to turn their backs on Friday, Jesus said, "Father, forgive them."

Prayer
Forgiving God, my shortcomings are many, but you remain steadfast in your love for me. Continue your tireless work in me so that I might become the servant you desire. AMEN.

Personal Reflection

....

....

....

....

Notes

Notes

MOVE · REFLECT DISCUSS

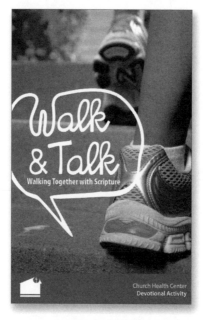

Walk & Talk: Walking Together with Scripture is a year-long walking Bible study and devotional that is specifically designed to be used while you walk with a friend, with a member of your congregation, or by yourself. Each devotional provides a scripture passage, a short reflection, a series of discussion questions and a closing prayer.

STORE.CHURCHHEALTHCENTER.ORG

INNOVATIVE · INSPIRATIONAL
KNOWLEDGEABLE · PRACTICAL

SUBSCRIBE TODAY!

Since its founding in 2008, *Church Health Reader* has grown from a startup website to an award-winning print and online publication. *Church Health Reader* encourages and equips people of faith to create and sustain Christian ministries of health, healing and wholeness. Our quarterly publication publishes inspirational and innovative resources drawn from knowledgeable sources, and offers practical ways to create happier, healthier communities.

CHREADER.ORG

Walking to Health, Walking to Faith

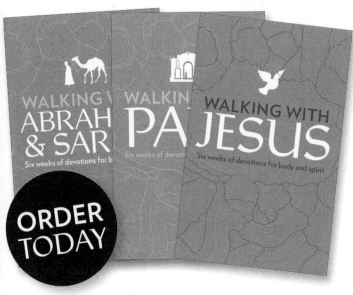

Work on health goals for six weeks while meditating on Scripture readings that follow the walking routes of Abraham and Sarah, Jesus, or Paul.